Usborne Little Wipe-Clean
Word Book
Outdoors

Illustrated by Marta Cabrol

Designed by Yasmin Faulkner
Edited by Felicity Brooks

Trace over all the words in this book.

duck

pond

Out and about

sun

cloud

rain

rainbow

puddle

log

gate   bridge

rock   bush

lake   hill

On the farm

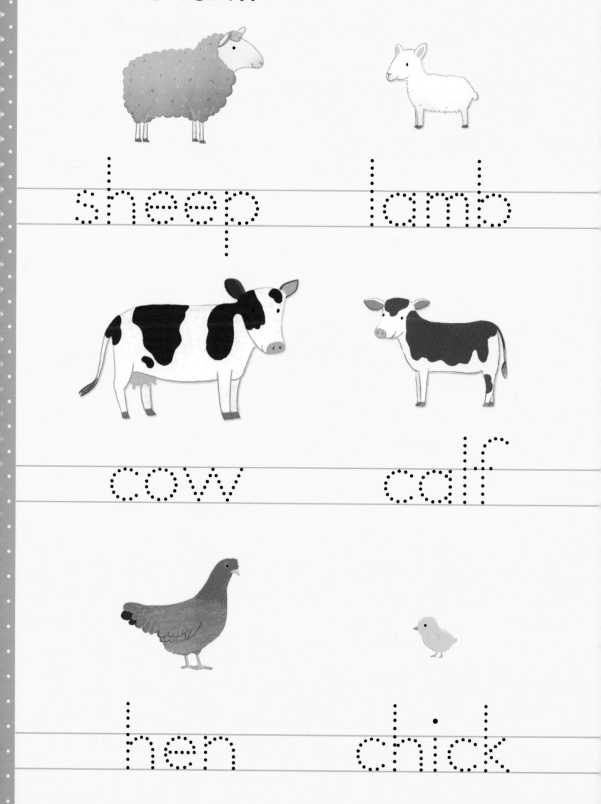

sheep

lamb

cow

calf

hen

chick

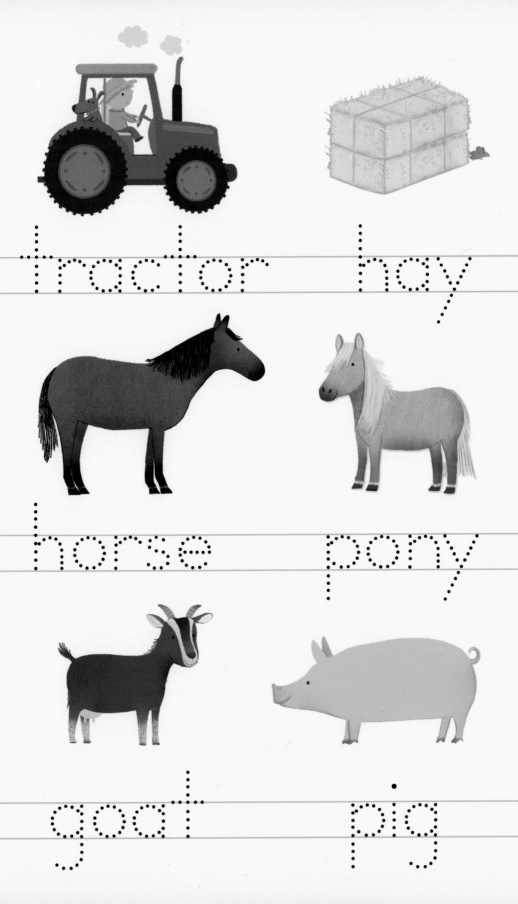

tractor hay

horse pony

goat pig

Lots of bugs

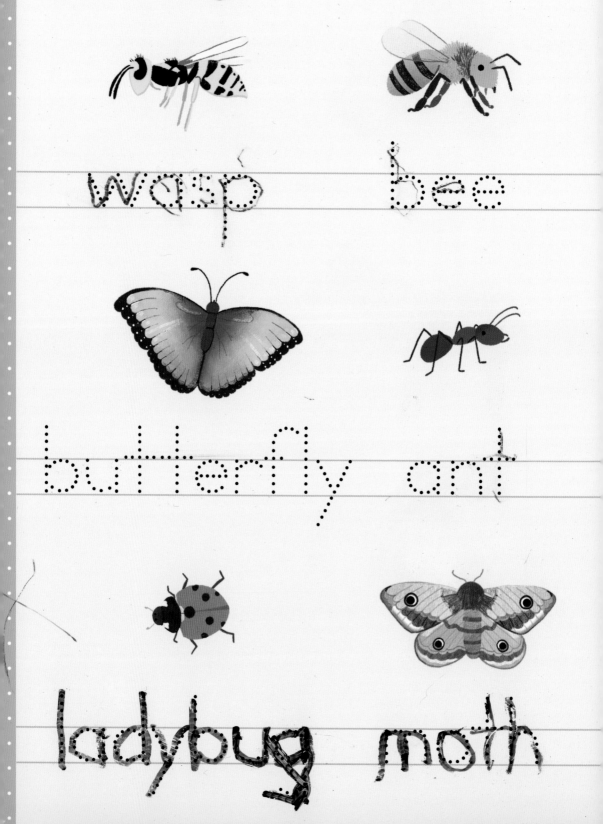

wasp   bee

butterfly   ant

ladybug   moth

beetle   spider

slug   worm

caterpillar fly

Woodland animals

squirrel   rabbit

hedgehog   fox

badger   mole

bear cub deer

shrew wolf

bat raccoon

By the river

toad   frog

dragonfly newt

duck   lily pads

At the seaside

gull   seaweed

starfish   shells

mussel   crab

The wildlife park

penguin   lemur

sloth   meerkat

gorilla   elephant

crocodile   tiger

lion   panda

zebra   monkey

All kinds of birds

swallow parrot

magpie pigeon

crow blackbird

pheasant owl

eagle hawk

swan flamingo

Pretty flowers

daisy   dandelion

poppy   bluebell

lavender   pansy

sunflower rose

tulip buttercup

daffodil crocus

Leaves

oak

ash

maple

holly

beech

fern

Seasons

spring   summer

fall   winter

Nature trail

twig   pinecone

acorn   nutshell

feather   catkins